PASSWORD

WEBSITE		WEBSITE	
EMAIL		EMAIL	
CONTACT		CONTACT	
PASSWORD		PASSWORD	
NOTES		NOTES	

WEBSITE		WEBSITE	
EMAIL		EMAIL	
CONTACT		CONTACT	
PASSWORD		PASSWORD	
NOTES		NOTES	

WEBSITE		WEBSITE	
EMAIL		EMAIL	
CONTACT		CONTACT	
PASSWORD		PASSWORD	
NOTES		NOTES	

WEBSITE		WEBSITE	
EMAIL		EMAIL	
CONTACT		CONTACT	
PASSWORD		PASSWORD	
NOTES		NOTES	

PASSWORD TRACKER

WEBSITE

EMAIL

CONTACT

PASSWORD

NOTES

WEBSITE

EMAIL

CONTACT

PASSWORD

NOTES

WEBSITE

EMAIL

CONTACT

PASSWORD

NOTES

WEBSITE

EMAIL

CONTACT

PASSWORD

NOTES

WEBSITE

EMAIL

CONTACT

PASSWORD

NOTES

WEBSITE

EMAIL

CONTACT

PASSWORD

NOTES

WEBSITE

EMAIL

CONTACT

PASSWORD

NOTES

WEBSITE

EMAIL

CONTACT

PASSWORD

NOTES

PASSWORD TRACKER

WEBSITE

EMAIL

CONTACT

PASSWORD

NOTES

WEBSITE

EMAIL

CONTACT

PASSWORD

NOTES

WEBSITE

EMAIL

CONTACT

PASSWORD

NOTES

WEBSITE

EMAIL

CONTACT

PASSWORD

NOTES

WEBSITE

EMAIL

CONTACT

PASSWORD

NOTES

WEBSITE

EMAIL

CONTACT

PASSWORD

NOTES

WEBSITE

EMAIL

CONTACT

PASSWORD

NOTES

WEBSITE

EMAIL

CONTACT

PASSWORD

NOTES

PASSWORD TRACKER

WEBSITE	
EMAIL	
CONTACT	
PASSWORD	
NOTES	

WEBSITE	
EMAIL	
CONTACT	
PASSWORD	
NOTES	

WEBSITE	
EMAIL	
CONTACT	
PASSWORD	
NOTES	

WEBSITE	
EMAIL	
CONTACT	
PASSWORD	
NOTES	

WEBSITE	
EMAIL	
CONTACT	
PASSWORD	
NOTES	

WEBSITE	
EMAIL	
CONTACT	
PASSWORD	
NOTES	

WEBSITE	
EMAIL	
CONTACT	
PASSWORD	
NOTES	

WEBSITE	
EMAIL	
CONTACT	
PASSWORD	
NOTES	

PASSWORD TRACKER

WEBSITE

EMAIL

CONTACT

PASSWORD

NOTES

WEBSITE

EMAIL

CONTACT

PASSWORD

NOTES

WEBSITE

EMAIL

CONTACT

PASSWORD

NOTES

WEBSITE

EMAIL

CONTACT

PASSWORD

NOTES

WEBSITE

EMAIL

CONTACT

PASSWORD

NOTES

WEBSITE

EMAIL

CONTACT

PASSWORD

NOTES

WEBSITE

EMAIL

CONTACT

PASSWORD

NOTES

WEBSITE

EMAIL

CONTACT

PASSWORD

NOTES

PASSWORD TRACKER

WEBSITE

EMAIL

CONTACT

PASSWORD

NOTES

WEBSITE

EMAIL

CONTACT

PASSWORD

NOTES

WEBSITE

EMAIL

CONTACT

PASSWORD

NOTES

WEBSITE

EMAIL

CONTACT

PASSWORD

NOTES

WEBSITE

EMAIL

CONTACT

PASSWORD

NOTES

WEBSITE

EMAIL

CONTACT

PASSWORD

NOTES

WEBSITE

EMAIL

CONTACT

PASSWORD

NOTES

WEBSITE

EMAIL

CONTACT

PASSWORD

NOTES

PASSWORD TRACKER

WEBSITE	
EMAIL	
CONTACT	
PASSWORD	
NOTES	

WEBSITE	
EMAIL	
CONTACT	
PASSWORD	
NOTES	

WEBSITE	
EMAIL	
CONTACT	
PASSWORD	
NOTES	

WEBSITE	
EMAIL	
CONTACT	
PASSWORD	
NOTES	

WEBSITE	
EMAIL	
CONTACT	
PASSWORD	
NOTES	

WEBSITE	
EMAIL	
CONTACT	
PASSWORD	
NOTES	

WEBSITE	
EMAIL	
CONTACT	
PASSWORD	
NOTES	

WEBSITE	
EMAIL	
CONTACT	
PASSWORD	
NOTES	

PASSWORD TRACKER

WEBSITE	
EMAIL	
CONTACT	
PASSWORD	
NOTES	

WEBSITE	
EMAIL	
CONTACT	
PASSWORD	
NOTES	

WEBSITE	
EMAIL	
CONTACT	
PASSWORD	
NOTES	

WEBSITE	
EMAIL	
CONTACT	
PASSWORD	
NOTES	

WEBSITE	
EMAIL	
CONTACT	
PASSWORD	
NOTES	

WEBSITE	
EMAIL	
CONTACT	
PASSWORD	
NOTES	

WEBSITE	
EMAIL	
CONTACT	
PASSWORD	
NOTES	

WEBSITE	
EMAIL	
CONTACT	
PASSWORD	
NOTES	

PASSWORD TRACKER

WEBSITE

EMAIL

CONTACT

PASSWORD

NOTES

WEBSITE

EMAIL

CONTACT

PASSWORD

NOTES

WEBSITE

EMAIL

CONTACT

PASSWORD

NOTES

WEBSITE

EMAIL

CONTACT

PASSWORD

NOTES

WEBSITE

EMAIL

CONTACT

PASSWORD

NOTES

WEBSITE

EMAIL

CONTACT

PASSWORD

NOTES

WEBSITE

EMAIL

CONTACT

PASSWORD

NOTES

WEBSITE

EMAIL

CONTACT

PASSWORD

NOTES

PASSWORD TRACKER

WEBSITE

EMAIL

CONTACT

PASSWORD

NOTES

WEBSITE

EMAIL

CONTACT

PASSWORD

NOTES

WEBSITE

EMAIL

CONTACT

PASSWORD

NOTES

WEBSITE

EMAIL

CONTACT

PASSWORD

NOTES

WEBSITE

EMAIL

CONTACT

PASSWORD

NOTES

WEBSITE

EMAIL

CONTACT

PASSWORD

NOTES

WEBSITE

EMAIL

CONTACT

PASSWORD

NOTES

WEBSITE

EMAIL

CONTACT

PASSWORD

NOTES

PASSWORD TRACKER

WEBSITE

EMAIL

CONTACT

PASSWORD

NOTES

WEBSITE

EMAIL

CONTACT

PASSWORD

NOTES

WEBSITE

EMAIL

CONTACT

PASSWORD

NOTES

WEBSITE

EMAIL

CONTACT

PASSWORD

NOTES

WEBSITE

EMAIL

CONTACT

PASSWORD

NOTES

WEBSITE

EMAIL

CONTACT

PASSWORD

NOTES

WEBSITE

EMAIL

CONTACT

PASSWORD

NOTES

WEBSITE

EMAIL

CONTACT

PASSWORD

NOTES

PASSWORD TRACKER

WEBSITE	
EMAIL	
CONTACT	
PASSWORD	
NOTES	

WEBSITE	
EMAIL	
CONTACT	
PASSWORD	
NOTES	

WEBSITE	
EMAIL	
CONTACT	
PASSWORD	
NOTES	

WEBSITE	
EMAIL	
CONTACT	
PASSWORD	
NOTES	

WEBSITE	
EMAIL	
CONTACT	
PASSWORD	
NOTES	

WEBSITE	
EMAIL	
CONTACT	
PASSWORD	
NOTES	

WEBSITE	
EMAIL	
CONTACT	
PASSWORD	
NOTES	

WEBSITE	
EMAIL	
CONTACT	
PASSWORD	
NOTES	

PASSWORD TRACKER

WEBSITE	
EMAIL	
CONTACT	
PASSWORD	
NOTES	

WEBSITE	
EMAIL	
CONTACT	
PASSWORD	
NOTES	

WEBSITE	
EMAIL	
CONTACT	
PASSWORD	
NOTES	

WEBSITE	
EMAIL	
CONTACT	
PASSWORD	
NOTES	

WEBSITE	
EMAIL	
CONTACT	
PASSWORD	
NOTES	

WEBSITE	
EMAIL	
CONTACT	
PASSWORD	
NOTES	

WEBSITE	
EMAIL	
CONTACT	
PASSWORD	
NOTES	

WEBSITE	
EMAIL	
CONTACT	
PASSWORD	
NOTES	

PASSWORD TRACKER

WEBSITE	
EMAIL	
CONTACT	
PASSWORD	
NOTES	

WEBSITE	
EMAIL	
CONTACT	
PASSWORD	
NOTES	

WEBSITE	
EMAIL	
CONTACT	
PASSWORD	
NOTES	

WEBSITE	
EMAIL	
CONTACT	
PASSWORD	
NOTES	

WEBSITE	
EMAIL	
CONTACT	
PASSWORD	
NOTES	

WEBSITE	
EMAIL	
CONTACT	
PASSWORD	
NOTES	

WEBSITE	
EMAIL	
CONTACT	
PASSWORD	
NOTES	

WEBSITE	
EMAIL	
CONTACT	
PASSWORD	
NOTES	

PASSWORD TRACKER

WEBSITE	WEBSITE
EMAIL	EMAIL
CONTACT	CONTACT
PASSWORD	PASSWORD
NOTES	NOTES

WEBSITE	WEBSITE
EMAIL	EMAIL
CONTACT	CONTACT
PASSWORD	PASSWORD
NOTES	NOTES

WEBSITE	WEBSITE
EMAIL	EMAIL
CONTACT	CONTACT
PASSWORD	PASSWORD
NOTES	NOTES

WEBSITE	WEBSITE
EMAIL	EMAIL
CONTACT	CONTACT
PASSWORD	PASSWORD
NOTES	NOTES

PASSWORD TRACKER

WEBSITE	
EMAIL	
CONTACT	
PASSWORD	
NOTES	

WEBSITE	
EMAIL	
CONTACT	
PASSWORD	
NOTES	

WEBSITE	
EMAIL	
CONTACT	
PASSWORD	
NOTES	

WEBSITE	
EMAIL	
CONTACT	
PASSWORD	
NOTES	

WEBSITE	
EMAIL	
CONTACT	
PASSWORD	
NOTES	

WEBSITE	
EMAIL	
CONTACT	
PASSWORD	
NOTES	

WEBSITE	
EMAIL	
CONTACT	
PASSWORD	
NOTES	

WEBSITE	
EMAIL	
CONTACT	
PASSWORD	
NOTES	

PASSWORD TRACKER

WEBSITE

EMAIL

CONTACT

PASSWORD

NOTES

WEBSITE

EMAIL

CONTACT

PASSWORD

NOTES

WEBSITE

EMAIL

CONTACT

PASSWORD

NOTES

WEBSITE

EMAIL

CONTACT

PASSWORD

NOTES

WEBSITE

EMAIL

CONTACT

PASSWORD

NOTES

WEBSITE

EMAIL

CONTACT

PASSWORD

NOTES

WEBSITE

EMAIL

CONTACT

PASSWORD

NOTES

WEBSITE

EMAIL

CONTACT

PASSWORD

NOTES

PASSWORD TRACKER

WEBSITE	
EMAIL	
CONTACT	
PASSWORD	
NOTES	

WEBSITE	
EMAIL	
CONTACT	
PASSWORD	
NOTES	

WEBSITE	
EMAIL	
CONTACT	
PASSWORD	
NOTES	

WEBSITE	
EMAIL	
CONTACT	
PASSWORD	
NOTES	

WEBSITE	
EMAIL	
CONTACT	
PASSWORD	
NOTES	

WEBSITE	
EMAIL	
CONTACT	
PASSWORD	
NOTES	

WEBSITE	
EMAIL	
CONTACT	
PASSWORD	
NOTES	

WEBSITE	
EMAIL	
CONTACT	
PASSWORD	
NOTES	

PASSWORD TRACKER

WEBSITE	
EMAIL	
CONTACT	
PASSWORD	
NOTES	

WEBSITE	
EMAIL	
CONTACT	
PASSWORD	
NOTES	

WEBSITE	
EMAIL	
CONTACT	
PASSWORD	
NOTES	

WEBSITE	
EMAIL	
CONTACT	
PASSWORD	
NOTES	

WEBSITE	
EMAIL	
CONTACT	
PASSWORD	
NOTES	

WEBSITE	
EMAIL	
CONTACT	
PASSWORD	
NOTES	

WEBSITE	
EMAIL	
CONTACT	
PASSWORD	
NOTES	

WEBSITE	
EMAIL	
CONTACT	
PASSWORD	
NOTES	

PASSWORD TRACKER

WEBSITE	
EMAIL	
CONTACT	
PASSWORD	
NOTES	

WEBSITE	
EMAIL	
CONTACT	
PASSWORD	
NOTES	

WEBSITE	
EMAIL	
CONTACT	
PASSWORD	
NOTES	

WEBSITE	
EMAIL	
CONTACT	
PASSWORD	
NOTES	

WEBSITE	
EMAIL	
CONTACT	
PASSWORD	
NOTES	

WEBSITE	
EMAIL	
CONTACT	
PASSWORD	
NOTES	

WEBSITE	
EMAIL	
CONTACT	
PASSWORD	
NOTES	

WEBSITE	
EMAIL	
CONTACT	
PASSWORD	
NOTES	

PASSWORD TRACKER

WEBSITE

EMAIL

CONTACT

PASSWORD

NOTES

WEBSITE

EMAIL

CONTACT

PASSWORD

NOTES

WEBSITE

EMAIL

CONTACT

PASSWORD

NOTES

WEBSITE

EMAIL

CONTACT

PASSWORD

NOTES

WEBSITE

EMAIL

CONTACT

PASSWORD

NOTES

WEBSITE

EMAIL

CONTACT

PASSWORD

NOTES

WEBSITE

EMAIL

CONTACT

PASSWORD

NOTES

WEBSITE

EMAIL

CONTACT

PASSWORD

NOTES

PASSWORD TRACKER

WEBSITE

EMAIL

CONTACT

PASSWORD

NOTES

WEBSITE

EMAIL

CONTACT

PASSWORD

NOTES

WEBSITE

EMAIL

CONTACT

PASSWORD

NOTES

WEBSITE

EMAIL

CONTACT

PASSWORD

NOTES

WEBSITE

EMAIL

CONTACT

PASSWORD

NOTES

WEBSITE

EMAIL

CONTACT

PASSWORD

NOTES

WEBSITE

EMAIL

CONTACT

PASSWORD

NOTES

WEBSITE

EMAIL

CONTACT

PASSWORD

NOTES

PASSWORD TRACKER

WEBSITE	WEBSITE
EMAIL	EMAIL
CONTACT	CONTACT
PASSWORD	PASSWORD
NOTES	NOTES

WEBSITE	WEBSITE
EMAIL	EMAIL
CONTACT	CONTACT
PASSWORD	PASSWORD
NOTES	NOTES

WEBSITE	WEBSITE
EMAIL	EMAIL
CONTACT	CONTACT
PASSWORD	PASSWORD
NOTES	NOTES

WEBSITE	WEBSITE
EMAIL	EMAIL
CONTACT	CONTACT
PASSWORD	PASSWORD
NOTES	NOTES

PASSWORD TRACKER

WEBSITE	
EMAIL	
CONTACT	
PASSWORD	
NOTES	

WEBSITE	
EMAIL	
CONTACT	
PASSWORD	
NOTES	

WEBSITE	
EMAIL	
CONTACT	
PASSWORD	
NOTES	

WEBSITE	
EMAIL	
CONTACT	
PASSWORD	
NOTES	

WEBSITE	
EMAIL	
CONTACT	
PASSWORD	
NOTES	

WEBSITE	
EMAIL	
CONTACT	
PASSWORD	
NOTES	

WEBSITE	
EMAIL	
CONTACT	
PASSWORD	
NOTES	

WEBSITE	
EMAIL	
CONTACT	
PASSWORD	
NOTES	

PASSWORD TRACKER

WEBSITE	WEBSITE
EMAIL	EMAIL
CONTACT	CONTACT
PASSWORD	PASSWORD
NOTES	NOTES

WEBSITE	WEBSITE
EMAIL	EMAIL
CONTACT	CONTACT
PASSWORD	PASSWORD
NOTES	NOTES

WEBSITE	WEBSITE
EMAIL	EMAIL
CONTACT	CONTACT
PASSWORD	PASSWORD
NOTES	NOTES

WEBSITE	WEBSITE
EMAIL	EMAIL
CONTACT	CONTACT
PASSWORD	PASSWORD
NOTES	NOTES

PASSWORD TRACKER

WEBSITE	
EMAIL	
CONTACT	
PASSWORD	
NOTES	

WEBSITE	
EMAIL	
CONTACT	
PASSWORD	
NOTES	

WEBSITE	
EMAIL	
CONTACT	
PASSWORD	
NOTES	

WEBSITE	
EMAIL	
CONTACT	
PASSWORD	
NOTES	

WEBSITE	
EMAIL	
CONTACT	
PASSWORD	
NOTES	

WEBSITE	
EMAIL	
CONTACT	
PASSWORD	
NOTES	

WEBSITE	
EMAIL	
CONTACT	
PASSWORD	
NOTES	

WEBSITE	
EMAIL	
CONTACT	
PASSWORD	
NOTES	

PASSWORD TRACKER

WEBSITE	
EMAIL	
CONTACT	
PASSWORD	
NOTES	

WEBSITE	
EMAIL	
CONTACT	
PASSWORD	
NOTES	

WEBSITE	
EMAIL	
CONTACT	
PASSWORD	
NOTES	

WEBSITE	
EMAIL	
CONTACT	
PASSWORD	
NOTES	

WEBSITE	
EMAIL	
CONTACT	
PASSWORD	
NOTES	

WEBSITE	
EMAIL	
CONTACT	
PASSWORD	
NOTES	

WEBSITE	
EMAIL	
CONTACT	
PASSWORD	
NOTES	

WEBSITE	
EMAIL	
CONTACT	
PASSWORD	
NOTES	

PASSWORD TRACKER

WEBSITE

EMAIL

CONTACT

PASSWORD

NOTES

WEBSITE

EMAIL

CONTACT

PASSWORD

NOTES

WEBSITE

EMAIL

CONTACT

PASSWORD

NOTES

WEBSITE

EMAIL

CONTACT

PASSWORD

NOTES

WEBSITE

EMAIL

CONTACT

PASSWORD

NOTES

WEBSITE

EMAIL

CONTACT

PASSWORD

NOTES

WEBSITE

EMAIL

CONTACT

PASSWORD

NOTES

WEBSITE

EMAIL

CONTACT

PASSWORD

NOTES

PASSWORD TRACKER

WEBSITE	
EMAIL	
CONTACT	
PASSWORD	
NOTES	

WEBSITE	
EMAIL	
CONTACT	
PASSWORD	
NOTES	

WEBSITE	
EMAIL	
CONTACT	
PASSWORD	
NOTES	

WEBSITE	
EMAIL	
CONTACT	
PASSWORD	
NOTES	

WEBSITE	
EMAIL	
CONTACT	
PASSWORD	
NOTES	

WEBSITE	
EMAIL	
CONTACT	
PASSWORD	
NOTES	

WEBSITE	
EMAIL	
CONTACT	
PASSWORD	
NOTES	

WEBSITE	
EMAIL	
CONTACT	
PASSWORD	
NOTES	

PASSWORD TRACKER

WEBSITE	
EMAIL	
CONTACT	
PASSWORD	
NOTES	

WEBSITE	
EMAIL	
CONTACT	
PASSWORD	
NOTES	

WEBSITE	
EMAIL	
CONTACT	
PASSWORD	
NOTES	

WEBSITE	
EMAIL	
CONTACT	
PASSWORD	
NOTES	

WEBSITE	
EMAIL	
CONTACT	
PASSWORD	
NOTES	

WEBSITE	
EMAIL	
CONTACT	
PASSWORD	
NOTES	

WEBSITE	
EMAIL	
CONTACT	
PASSWORD	
NOTES	

WEBSITE	
EMAIL	
CONTACT	
PASSWORD	
NOTES	

PASSWORD TRACKER

WEBSITE

EMAIL

CONTACT

PASSWORD

NOTES

WEBSITE

EMAIL

CONTACT

PASSWORD

NOTES

WEBSITE

EMAIL

CONTACT

PASSWORD

NOTES

WEBSITE

EMAIL

CONTACT

PASSWORD

NOTES

WEBSITE

EMAIL

CONTACT

PASSWORD

NOTES

WEBSITE

EMAIL

CONTACT

PASSWORD

NOTES

WEBSITE

EMAIL

CONTACT

PASSWORD

NOTES

WEBSITE

EMAIL

CONTACT

PASSWORD

NOTES

PASSWORD TRACKER

WEBSITE	
EMAIL	
CONTACT	
PASSWORD	
NOTES	

WEBSITE	
EMAIL	
CONTACT	
PASSWORD	
NOTES	

WEBSITE	
EMAIL	
CONTACT	
PASSWORD	
NOTES	

WEBSITE	
EMAIL	
CONTACT	
PASSWORD	
NOTES	

WEBSITE	
EMAIL	
CONTACT	
PASSWORD	
NOTES	

WEBSITE	
EMAIL	
CONTACT	
PASSWORD	
NOTES	

WEBSITE	
EMAIL	
CONTACT	
PASSWORD	
NOTES	

WEBSITE	
EMAIL	
CONTACT	
PASSWORD	
NOTES	

PASSWORD TRACKER

WEBSITE

EMAIL

CONTACT

PASSWORD

NOTES

WEBSITE

EMAIL

CONTACT

PASSWORD

NOTES

WEBSITE

EMAIL

CONTACT

PASSWORD

NOTES

WEBSITE

EMAIL

CONTACT

PASSWORD

NOTES

WEBSITE

EMAIL

CONTACT

PASSWORD

NOTES

WEBSITE

EMAIL

CONTACT

PASSWORD

NOTES

WEBSITE

EMAIL

CONTACT

PASSWORD

NOTES

WEBSITE

EMAIL

CONTACT

PASSWORD

NOTES

PASSWORD TRACKER

WEBSITE	
EMAIL	
CONTACT	
PASSWORD	
NOTES	

WEBSITE	
EMAIL	
CONTACT	
PASSWORD	
NOTES	

WEBSITE	
EMAIL	
CONTACT	
PASSWORD	
NOTES	

WEBSITE	
EMAIL	
CONTACT	
PASSWORD	
NOTES	

WEBSITE	
EMAIL	
CONTACT	
PASSWORD	
NOTES	

WEBSITE	
EMAIL	
CONTACT	
PASSWORD	
NOTES	

WEBSITE	
EMAIL	
CONTACT	
PASSWORD	
NOTES	

WEBSITE	
EMAIL	
CONTACT	
PASSWORD	
NOTES	

PASSWORD TRACKER

WEBSITE	WEBSITE
EMAIL	EMAIL
CONTACT	CONTACT
PASSWORD	PASSWORD
NOTES	NOTES

WEBSITE	WEBSITE
EMAIL	EMAIL
CONTACT	CONTACT
PASSWORD	PASSWORD
NOTES	NOTES

WEBSITE	WEBSITE
EMAIL	EMAIL
CONTACT	CONTACT
PASSWORD	PASSWORD
NOTES	NOTES

WEBSITE	WEBSITE
EMAIL	EMAIL
CONTACT	CONTACT
PASSWORD	PASSWORD
NOTES	NOTES

PASSWORD TRACKER

WEBSITE	
EMAIL	
CONTACT	
PASSWORD	
NOTES	

WEBSITE	
EMAIL	
CONTACT	
PASSWORD	
NOTES	

WEBSITE	
EMAIL	
CONTACT	
PASSWORD	
NOTES	

WEBSITE	
EMAIL	
CONTACT	
PASSWORD	
NOTES	

WEBSITE	
EMAIL	
CONTACT	
PASSWORD	
NOTES	

WEBSITE	
EMAIL	
CONTACT	
PASSWORD	
NOTES	

WEBSITE	
EMAIL	
CONTACT	
PASSWORD	
NOTES	

WEBSITE	
EMAIL	
CONTACT	
PASSWORD	
NOTES	

PASSWORD TRACKER

WEBSITE

EMAIL

CONTACT

PASSWORD

NOTES

WEBSITE

EMAIL

CONTACT

PASSWORD

NOTES

WEBSITE

EMAIL

CONTACT

PASSWORD

NOTES

WEBSITE

EMAIL

CONTACT

PASSWORD

NOTES

WEBSITE

EMAIL

CONTACT

PASSWORD

NOTES

WEBSITE

EMAIL

CONTACT

PASSWORD

NOTES

WEBSITE

EMAIL

CONTACT

PASSWORD

NOTES

WEBSITE

EMAIL

CONTACT

PASSWORD

NOTES

PASSWORD TRACKER

WEBSITE	
EMAIL	
CONTACT	
PASSWORD	
NOTES	

WEBSITE	
EMAIL	
CONTACT	
PASSWORD	
NOTES	

WEBSITE	
EMAIL	
CONTACT	
PASSWORD	
NOTES	

WEBSITE	
EMAIL	
CONTACT	
PASSWORD	
NOTES	

WEBSITE	
EMAIL	
CONTACT	
PASSWORD	
NOTES	

WEBSITE	
EMAIL	
CONTACT	
PASSWORD	
NOTES	

WEBSITE	
EMAIL	
CONTACT	
PASSWORD	
NOTES	

WEBSITE	
EMAIL	
CONTACT	
PASSWORD	
NOTES	

PASSWORD TRACKER

WEBSITE	
EMAIL	
CONTACT	
PASSWORD	
NOTES	

WEBSITE	
EMAIL	
CONTACT	
PASSWORD	
NOTES	

WEBSITE	
EMAIL	
CONTACT	
PASSWORD	
NOTES	

WEBSITE	
EMAIL	
CONTACT	
PASSWORD	
NOTES	

WEBSITE	
EMAIL	
CONTACT	
PASSWORD	
NOTES	

WEBSITE	
EMAIL	
CONTACT	
PASSWORD	
NOTES	

WEBSITE	
EMAIL	
CONTACT	
PASSWORD	
NOTES	

WEBSITE	
EMAIL	
CONTACT	
PASSWORD	
NOTES	

PASSWORD TRACKER

WEBSITE	
EMAIL	
CONTACT	
PASSWORD	
NOTES	

WEBSITE	
EMAIL	
CONTACT	
PASSWORD	
NOTES	

WEBSITE	
EMAIL	
CONTACT	
PASSWORD	
NOTES	

WEBSITE	
EMAIL	
CONTACT	
PASSWORD	
NOTES	

WEBSITE	
EMAIL	
CONTACT	
PASSWORD	
NOTES	

WEBSITE	
EMAIL	
CONTACT	
PASSWORD	
NOTES	

WEBSITE	
EMAIL	
CONTACT	
PASSWORD	
NOTES	

WEBSITE	
EMAIL	
CONTACT	
PASSWORD	
NOTES	

PASSWORD TRACKER

WEBSITE

EMAIL

CONTACT

PASSWORD

NOTES

WEBSITE

EMAIL

CONTACT

PASSWORD

NOTES

WEBSITE

EMAIL

CONTACT

PASSWORD

NOTES

WEBSITE

EMAIL

CONTACT

PASSWORD

NOTES

WEBSITE

EMAIL

CONTACT

PASSWORD

NOTES

WEBSITE

EMAIL

CONTACT

PASSWORD

NOTES

WEBSITE

EMAIL

CONTACT

PASSWORD

NOTES

WEBSITE

EMAIL

CONTACT

PASSWORD

NOTES

PASSWORD TRACKER

WEBSITE	
EMAIL	
CONTACT	
PASSWORD	
NOTES	

WEBSITE	
EMAIL	
CONTACT	
PASSWORD	
NOTES	

WEBSITE	
EMAIL	
CONTACT	
PASSWORD	
NOTES	

WEBSITE	
EMAIL	
CONTACT	
PASSWORD	
NOTES	

WEBSITE	
EMAIL	
CONTACT	
PASSWORD	
NOTES	

WEBSITE	
EMAIL	
CONTACT	
PASSWORD	
NOTES	

WEBSITE	
EMAIL	
CONTACT	
PASSWORD	
NOTES	

WEBSITE	
EMAIL	
CONTACT	
PASSWORD	
NOTES	

PASSWORD TRACKER

WEBSITE		WEBSITE	
EMAIL		EMAIL	
CONTACT		CONTACT	
PASSWORD		PASSWORD	
NOTES		NOTES	

WEBSITE		WEBSITE	
EMAIL		EMAIL	
CONTACT		CONTACT	
PASSWORD		PASSWORD	
NOTES		NOTES	

WEBSITE		WEBSITE	
EMAIL		EMAIL	
CONTACT		CONTACT	
PASSWORD		PASSWORD	
NOTES		NOTES	

WEBSITE		WEBSITE	
EMAIL		EMAIL	
CONTACT		CONTACT	
PASSWORD		PASSWORD	
NOTES		NOTES	

PASSWORD TRACKER

WEBSITE

EMAIL

CONTACT

PASSWORD

NOTES

WEBSITE

EMAIL

CONTACT

PASSWORD

NOTES

WEBSITE

EMAIL

CONTACT

PASSWORD

NOTES

WEBSITE

EMAIL

CONTACT

PASSWORD

NOTES

WEBSITE

EMAIL

CONTACT

PASSWORD

NOTES

WEBSITE

EMAIL

CONTACT

PASSWORD

NOTES

WEBSITE

EMAIL

CONTACT

PASSWORD

NOTES

WEBSITE

EMAIL

CONTACT

PASSWORD

NOTES

PASSWORD TRACKER

WEBSITE

EMAIL

CONTACT

PASSWORD

NOTES

WEBSITE

EMAIL

CONTACT

PASSWORD

NOTES

WEBSITE

EMAIL

CONTACT

PASSWORD

NOTES

WEBSITE

EMAIL

CONTACT

PASSWORD

NOTES

WEBSITE

EMAIL

CONTACT

PASSWORD

NOTES

WEBSITE

EMAIL

CONTACT

PASSWORD

NOTES

WEBSITE

EMAIL

CONTACT

PASSWORD

NOTES

WEBSITE

EMAIL

CONTACT

PASSWORD

NOTES

PASSWORD TRACKER

WEBSITE	
EMAIL	
CONTACT	
PASSWORD	
NOTES	

WEBSITE	
EMAIL	
CONTACT	
PASSWORD	
NOTES	

WEBSITE	
EMAIL	
CONTACT	
PASSWORD	
NOTES	

WEBSITE	
EMAIL	
CONTACT	
PASSWORD	
NOTES	

WEBSITE	
EMAIL	
CONTACT	
PASSWORD	
NOTES	

WEBSITE	
EMAIL	
CONTACT	
PASSWORD	
NOTES	

WEBSITE	
EMAIL	
CONTACT	
PASSWORD	
NOTES	

WEBSITE	
EMAIL	
CONTACT	
PASSWORD	
NOTES	

PASSWORD TRACKER

WEBSITE

EMAIL

CONTACT

PASSWORD

NOTES

WEBSITE

EMAIL

CONTACT

PASSWORD

NOTES

WEBSITE

EMAIL

CONTACT

PASSWORD

NOTES

WEBSITE

EMAIL

CONTACT

PASSWORD

NOTES

WEBSITE

EMAIL

CONTACT

PASSWORD

NOTES

WEBSITE

EMAIL

CONTACT

PASSWORD

NOTES

WEBSITE

EMAIL

CONTACT

PASSWORD

NOTES

WEBSITE

EMAIL

CONTACT

PASSWORD

NOTES

PASSWORD TRACKER

WEBSITE	
EMAIL	
CONTACT	
PASSWORD	
NOTES	

WEBSITE	
EMAIL	
CONTACT	
PASSWORD	
NOTES	

WEBSITE	
EMAIL	
CONTACT	
PASSWORD	
NOTES	

WEBSITE	
EMAIL	
CONTACT	
PASSWORD	
NOTES	

WEBSITE	
EMAIL	
CONTACT	
PASSWORD	
NOTES	

WEBSITE	
EMAIL	
CONTACT	
PASSWORD	
NOTES	

WEBSITE	
EMAIL	
CONTACT	
PASSWORD	
NOTES	

WEBSITE	
EMAIL	
CONTACT	
PASSWORD	
NOTES	

PASSWORD TRACKER

WEBSITE	
EMAIL	
CONTACT	
PASSWORD	
NOTES	

WEBSITE	
EMAIL	
CONTACT	
PASSWORD	
NOTES	

WEBSITE	
EMAIL	
CONTACT	
PASSWORD	
NOTES	

WEBSITE	
EMAIL	
CONTACT	
PASSWORD	
NOTES	

WEBSITE	
EMAIL	
CONTACT	
PASSWORD	
NOTES	

WEBSITE	
EMAIL	
CONTACT	
PASSWORD	
NOTES	

WEBSITE	
EMAIL	
CONTACT	
PASSWORD	
NOTES	

WEBSITE	
EMAIL	
CONTACT	
PASSWORD	
NOTES	

PASSWORD TRACKER

WEBSITE	
EMAIL	
CONTACT	
PASSWORD	
NOTES	

WEBSITE	
EMAIL	
CONTACT	
PASSWORD	
NOTES	

WEBSITE	
EMAIL	
CONTACT	
PASSWORD	
NOTES	

WEBSITE	
EMAIL	
CONTACT	
PASSWORD	
NOTES	

WEBSITE	
EMAIL	
CONTACT	
PASSWORD	
NOTES	

WEBSITE	
EMAIL	
CONTACT	
PASSWORD	
NOTES	

WEBSITE	
EMAIL	
CONTACT	
PASSWORD	
NOTES	

WEBSITE	
EMAIL	
CONTACT	
PASSWORD	
NOTES	

PASSWORD TRACKER

WEBSITE	
EMAIL	
CONTACT	
PASSWORD	
NOTES	

WEBSITE	
EMAIL	
CONTACT	
PASSWORD	
NOTES	

WEBSITE	
EMAIL	
CONTACT	
PASSWORD	
NOTES	

WEBSITE	
EMAIL	
CONTACT	
PASSWORD	
NOTES	

WEBSITE	
EMAIL	
CONTACT	
PASSWORD	
NOTES	

WEBSITE	
EMAIL	
CONTACT	
PASSWORD	
NOTES	

WEBSITE	
EMAIL	
CONTACT	
PASSWORD	
NOTES	

WEBSITE	
EMAIL	
CONTACT	
PASSWORD	
NOTES	

PASSWORD TRACKER

WEBSITE	
EMAIL	
CONTACT	
PASSWORD	
NOTES	

WEBSITE	
EMAIL	
CONTACT	
PASSWORD	
NOTES	

WEBSITE	
EMAIL	
CONTACT	
PASSWORD	
NOTES	

WEBSITE	
EMAIL	
CONTACT	
PASSWORD	
NOTES	

WEBSITE	
EMAIL	
CONTACT	
PASSWORD	
NOTES	

WEBSITE	
EMAIL	
CONTACT	
PASSWORD	
NOTES	

WEBSITE	
EMAIL	
CONTACT	
PASSWORD	
NOTES	

WEBSITE	
EMAIL	
CONTACT	
PASSWORD	
NOTES	

PASSWORD TRACKER

WEBSITE

EMAIL

CONTACT

PASSWORD

NOTES

WEBSITE

EMAIL

CONTACT

PASSWORD

NOTES

WEBSITE

EMAIL

CONTACT

PASSWORD

NOTES

WEBSITE

EMAIL

CONTACT

PASSWORD

NOTES

WEBSITE

EMAIL

CONTACT

PASSWORD

NOTES

WEBSITE

EMAIL

CONTACT

PASSWORD

NOTES

WEBSITE

EMAIL

CONTACT

PASSWORD

NOTES

WEBSITE

EMAIL

CONTACT

PASSWORD

NOTES

PASSWORD TRACKER

WEBSITE	
EMAIL	
CONTACT	
PASSWORD	
NOTES	

WEBSITE	
EMAIL	
CONTACT	
PASSWORD	
NOTES	

WEBSITE	
EMAIL	
CONTACT	
PASSWORD	
NOTES	

WEBSITE	
EMAIL	
CONTACT	
PASSWORD	
NOTES	

WEBSITE	
EMAIL	
CONTACT	
PASSWORD	
NOTES	

WEBSITE	
EMAIL	
CONTACT	
PASSWORD	
NOTES	

WEBSITE	
EMAIL	
CONTACT	
PASSWORD	
NOTES	

WEBSITE	
EMAIL	
CONTACT	
PASSWORD	
NOTES	

PASSWORD TRACKER

WEBSITE	WEBSITE
EMAIL	EMAIL
CONTACT	CONTACT
PASSWORD	PASSWORD
NOTES	NOTES

WEBSITE	WEBSITE
EMAIL	EMAIL
CONTACT	CONTACT
PASSWORD	PASSWORD
NOTES	NOTES

WEBSITE	WEBSITE
EMAIL	EMAIL
CONTACT	CONTACT
PASSWORD	PASSWORD
NOTES	NOTES

WEBSITE	WEBSITE
EMAIL	EMAIL
CONTACT	CONTACT
PASSWORD	PASSWORD
NOTES	NOTES

PASSWORD TRACKER

WEBSITE	
EMAIL	
CONTACT	
PASSWORD	
NOTES	

WEBSITE	
EMAIL	
CONTACT	
PASSWORD	
NOTES	

WEBSITE	
EMAIL	
CONTACT	
PASSWORD	
NOTES	

WEBSITE	
EMAIL	
CONTACT	
PASSWORD	
NOTES	

WEBSITE	
EMAIL	
CONTACT	
PASSWORD	
NOTES	

WEBSITE	
EMAIL	
CONTACT	
PASSWORD	
NOTES	

WEBSITE	
EMAIL	
CONTACT	
PASSWORD	
NOTES	

WEBSITE	
EMAIL	
CONTACT	
PASSWORD	
NOTES	

PASSWORD TRACKER

WEBSITE	WEBSITE
EMAIL	EMAIL
CONTACT	CONTACT
PASSWORD	PASSWORD
NOTES	NOTES

WEBSITE	WEBSITE
EMAIL	EMAIL
CONTACT	CONTACT
PASSWORD	PASSWORD
NOTES	NOTES

WEBSITE	WEBSITE
EMAIL	EMAIL
CONTACT	CONTACT
PASSWORD	PASSWORD
NOTES	NOTES

WEBSITE	WEBSITE
EMAIL	EMAIL
CONTACT	CONTACT
PASSWORD	PASSWORD
NOTES	NOTES

PASSWORD TRACKER

WEBSITE	
EMAIL	
CONTACT	
PASSWORD	
NOTES	

WEBSITE	
EMAIL	
CONTACT	
PASSWORD	
NOTES	

WEBSITE	
EMAIL	
CONTACT	
PASSWORD	
NOTES	

WEBSITE	
EMAIL	
CONTACT	
PASSWORD	
NOTES	

WEBSITE	
EMAIL	
CONTACT	
PASSWORD	
NOTES	

WEBSITE	
EMAIL	
CONTACT	
PASSWORD	
NOTES	

WEBSITE	
EMAIL	
CONTACT	
PASSWORD	
NOTES	

WEBSITE	
EMAIL	
CONTACT	
PASSWORD	
NOTES	

PASSWORD TRACKER

WEBSITE	
EMAIL	
CONTACT	
PASSWORD	
NOTES	

WEBSITE	
EMAIL	
CONTACT	
PASSWORD	
NOTES	

WEBSITE	
EMAIL	
CONTACT	
PASSWORD	
NOTES	

WEBSITE	
EMAIL	
CONTACT	
PASSWORD	
NOTES	

WEBSITE	
EMAIL	
CONTACT	
PASSWORD	
NOTES	

WEBSITE	
EMAIL	
CONTACT	
PASSWORD	
NOTES	

WEBSITE	
EMAIL	
CONTACT	
PASSWORD	
NOTES	

WEBSITE	
EMAIL	
CONTACT	
PASSWORD	
NOTES	

PASSWORD TRACKER

WEBSITE	
EMAIL	
CONTACT	
PASSWORD	
NOTES	

WEBSITE	
EMAIL	
CONTACT	
PASSWORD	
NOTES	

WEBSITE	
EMAIL	
CONTACT	
PASSWORD	
NOTES	

WEBSITE	
EMAIL	
CONTACT	
PASSWORD	
NOTES	

WEBSITE	
EMAIL	
CONTACT	
PASSWORD	
NOTES	

WEBSITE	
EMAIL	
CONTACT	
PASSWORD	
NOTES	

WEBSITE	
EMAIL	
CONTACT	
PASSWORD	
NOTES	

WEBSITE	
EMAIL	
CONTACT	
PASSWORD	
NOTES	

PASSWORD TRACKER

WEBSITE	WEBSITE
EMAIL	EMAIL
CONTACT	CONTACT
PASSWORD	PASSWORD
NOTES	NOTES

WEBSITE	WEBSITE
EMAIL	EMAIL
CONTACT	CONTACT
PASSWORD	PASSWORD
NOTES	NOTES

WEBSITE	WEBSITE
EMAIL	EMAIL
CONTACT	CONTACT
PASSWORD	PASSWORD
NOTES	NOTES

WEBSITE	WEBSITE
EMAIL	EMAIL
CONTACT	CONTACT
PASSWORD	PASSWORD
NOTES	NOTES

PASSWORD TRACKER

WEBSITE

EMAIL

CONTACT

PASSWORD

NOTES

WEBSITE

EMAIL

CONTACT

PASSWORD

NOTES

WEBSITE

EMAIL

CONTACT

PASSWORD

NOTES

WEBSITE

EMAIL

CONTACT

PASSWORD

NOTES

WEBSITE

EMAIL

CONTACT

PASSWORD

NOTES

WEBSITE

EMAIL

CONTACT

PASSWORD

NOTES

WEBSITE

EMAIL

CONTACT

PASSWORD

NOTES

WEBSITE

EMAIL

CONTACT

PASSWORD

NOTES

PASSWORD TRACKER

WEBSITE		WEBSITE	
EMAIL		EMAIL	
CONTACT		CONTACT	
PASSWORD		PASSWORD	
NOTES		NOTES	

WEBSITE		WEBSITE	
EMAIL		EMAIL	
CONTACT		CONTACT	
PASSWORD		PASSWORD	
NOTES		NOTES	

WEBSITE		WEBSITE	
EMAIL		EMAIL	
CONTACT		CONTACT	
PASSWORD		PASSWORD	
NOTES		NOTES	

WEBSITE		WEBSITE	
EMAIL		EMAIL	
CONTACT		CONTACT	
PASSWORD		PASSWORD	
NOTES		NOTES	

PASSWORD TRACKER

WEBSITE	
EMAIL	
CONTACT	
PASSWORD	
NOTES	

WEBSITE	
EMAIL	
CONTACT	
PASSWORD	
NOTES	

WEBSITE	
EMAIL	
CONTACT	
PASSWORD	
NOTES	

WEBSITE	
EMAIL	
CONTACT	
PASSWORD	
NOTES	

WEBSITE	
EMAIL	
CONTACT	
PASSWORD	
NOTES	

WEBSITE	
EMAIL	
CONTACT	
PASSWORD	
NOTES	

WEBSITE	
EMAIL	
CONTACT	
PASSWORD	
NOTES	

WEBSITE	
EMAIL	
CONTACT	
PASSWORD	
NOTES	

PASSWORD TRACKER

WEBSITE	WEBSITE
EMAIL	EMAIL
CONTACT	CONTACT
PASSWORD	PASSWORD
NOTES	NOTES

WEBSITE	WEBSITE
EMAIL	EMAIL
CONTACT	CONTACT
PASSWORD	PASSWORD
NOTES	NOTES

WEBSITE	WEBSITE
EMAIL	EMAIL
CONTACT	CONTACT
PASSWORD	PASSWORD
NOTES	NOTES

WEBSITE	WEBSITE
EMAIL	EMAIL
CONTACT	CONTACT
PASSWORD	PASSWORD
NOTES	NOTES

PASSWORD TRACKER

WEBSITE

EMAIL

CONTACT

PASSWORD

NOTES

WEBSITE

EMAIL

CONTACT

PASSWORD

NOTES

WEBSITE

EMAIL

CONTACT

PASSWORD

NOTES

WEBSITE

EMAIL

CONTACT

PASSWORD

NOTES

WEBSITE

EMAIL

CONTACT

PASSWORD

NOTES

WEBSITE

EMAIL

CONTACT

PASSWORD

NOTES

WEBSITE

EMAIL

CONTACT

PASSWORD

NOTES

WEBSITE

EMAIL

CONTACT

PASSWORD

NOTES

PASSWORD TRACKER

WEBSITE	
EMAIL	
CONTACT	
PASSWORD	
NOTES	

WEBSITE	
EMAIL	
CONTACT	
PASSWORD	
NOTES	

WEBSITE	
EMAIL	
CONTACT	
PASSWORD	
NOTES	

WEBSITE	
EMAIL	
CONTACT	
PASSWORD	
NOTES	

WEBSITE	
EMAIL	
CONTACT	
PASSWORD	
NOTES	

WEBSITE	
EMAIL	
CONTACT	
PASSWORD	
NOTES	

WEBSITE	
EMAIL	
CONTACT	
PASSWORD	
NOTES	

WEBSITE	
EMAIL	
CONTACT	
PASSWORD	
NOTES	

PASSWORD TRACKER

WEBSITE

EMAIL

CONTACT

PASSWORD

NOTES

WEBSITE

EMAIL

CONTACT

PASSWORD

NOTES

WEBSITE

EMAIL

CONTACT

PASSWORD

NOTES

WEBSITE

EMAIL

CONTACT

PASSWORD

NOTES

WEBSITE

EMAIL

CONTACT

PASSWORD

NOTES

WEBSITE

EMAIL

CONTACT

PASSWORD

NOTES

WEBSITE

EMAIL

CONTACT

PASSWORD

NOTES

WEBSITE

EMAIL

CONTACT

PASSWORD

NOTES

PASSWORD TRACKER

WEBSITE	WEBSITE
EMAIL	EMAIL
CONTACT	CONTACT
PASSWORD	PASSWORD
NOTES	NOTES

WEBSITE	WEBSITE
EMAIL	EMAIL
CONTACT	CONTACT
PASSWORD	PASSWORD
NOTES	NOTES

WEBSITE	WEBSITE
EMAIL	EMAIL
CONTACT	CONTACT
PASSWORD	PASSWORD
NOTES	NOTES

WEBSITE	WEBSITE
EMAIL	EMAIL
CONTACT	CONTACT
PASSWORD	PASSWORD
NOTES	NOTES

PASSWORD TRACKER

WEBSITE	
EMAIL	
CONTACT	
PASSWORD	
NOTES	

WEBSITE	
EMAIL	
CONTACT	
PASSWORD	
NOTES	

WEBSITE	
EMAIL	
CONTACT	
PASSWORD	
NOTES	

WEBSITE	
EMAIL	
CONTACT	
PASSWORD	
NOTES	

WEBSITE	
EMAIL	
CONTACT	
PASSWORD	
NOTES	

WEBSITE	
EMAIL	
CONTACT	
PASSWORD	
NOTES	

WEBSITE	
EMAIL	
CONTACT	
PASSWORD	
NOTES	

WEBSITE	
EMAIL	
CONTACT	
PASSWORD	
NOTES	

PASSWORD TRACKER

WEBSITE	WEBSITE
EMAIL	EMAIL
CONTACT	CONTACT
PASSWORD	PASSWORD
NOTES	NOTES

WEBSITE	WEBSITE
EMAIL	EMAIL
CONTACT	CONTACT
PASSWORD	PASSWORD
NOTES	NOTES

WEBSITE	WEBSITE
EMAIL	EMAIL
CONTACT	CONTACT
PASSWORD	PASSWORD
NOTES	NOTES

WEBSITE	WEBSITE
EMAIL	EMAIL
CONTACT	CONTACT
PASSWORD	PASSWORD
NOTES	NOTES

PASSWORD TRACKER

WEBSITE	WEBSITE
EMAIL	EMAIL
CONTACT	CONTACT
PASSWORD	PASSWORD
NOTES	NOTES

WEBSITE	WEBSITE
EMAIL	EMAIL
CONTACT	CONTACT
PASSWORD	PASSWORD
NOTES	NOTES

WEBSITE	WEBSITE
EMAIL	EMAIL
CONTACT	CONTACT
PASSWORD	PASSWORD
NOTES	NOTES

WEBSITE	WEBSITE
EMAIL	EMAIL
CONTACT	CONTACT
PASSWORD	PASSWORD
NOTES	NOTES

PASSWORD TRACKER

WEBSITE

EMAIL

CONTACT

PASSWORD

NOTES

WEBSITE

EMAIL

CONTACT

PASSWORD

NOTES

WEBSITE

EMAIL

CONTACT

PASSWORD

NOTES

WEBSITE

EMAIL

CONTACT

PASSWORD

NOTES

WEBSITE

EMAIL

CONTACT

PASSWORD

NOTES

WEBSITE

EMAIL

CONTACT

PASSWORD

NOTES

WEBSITE

EMAIL

CONTACT

PASSWORD

NOTES

WEBSITE

EMAIL

CONTACT

PASSWORD

NOTES

PASSWORD TRACKER

WEBSITE

EMAIL

CONTACT

PASSWORD

NOTES

WEBSITE

EMAIL

CONTACT

PASSWORD

NOTES

WEBSITE

EMAIL

CONTACT

PASSWORD

NOTES

WEBSITE

EMAIL

CONTACT

PASSWORD

NOTES

WEBSITE

EMAIL

CONTACT

PASSWORD

NOTES

WEBSITE

EMAIL

CONTACT

PASSWORD

NOTES

WEBSITE

EMAIL

CONTACT

PASSWORD

NOTES

WEBSITE

EMAIL

CONTACT

PASSWORD

NOTES

PASSWORD TRACKER

WEBSITE	WEBSITE
EMAIL	EMAIL
CONTACT	CONTACT
PASSWORD	PASSWORD
NOTES	NOTES

WEBSITE	WEBSITE
EMAIL	EMAIL
CONTACT	CONTACT
PASSWORD	PASSWORD
NOTES	NOTES

WEBSITE	WEBSITE
EMAIL	EMAIL
CONTACT	CONTACT
PASSWORD	PASSWORD
NOTES	NOTES

WEBSITE	WEBSITE
EMAIL	EMAIL
CONTACT	CONTACT
PASSWORD	PASSWORD
NOTES	NOTES

Made in United States
North Haven, CT
15 June 2022